Cicada: Exotic Views

Written By:
Davy Shian
Illustrations By:
Wang"王星"Xing

Hebei Fine Arts Publishing House

Cicada: Exotic Views

By studying cicadas, we see that even trivial things can be viewed from many different perspectives.

This book is dedicated to those who are interested in cicadas especially the ones who have taken pictures and written on the subject.

Author's Note and Acknowledgements

Cicadas are found in many countries all over the world. People recognize cicadas by the loud sounds they produce. Other than knowing what they are, it has been my experience that most people know little else. When asked, some American children thought the "cicada sound" was made by birds. When showed cicadas, some American friends were disgusted by their size and appearance.

I love cicadas. When I learned that so many people had fears and negative images of cicadas, I wanted to do something to encourage people to see the beauty and wonder of these creatures. I have chosen to use a cartoon format to keep the information light and fun.

If I cannot change people's views on cicadas, I hope to at least entertain them and let them recognize that there are other views. I also have included photos and background information so the reader can see cicadas up close and learn more about them. This book is not just for our American friends and audience; it is also for people in other countries who do not have the 17-year cicadas (we will learn more about these creatures later). So, this book is planned to be provided in several different languages. I am also taking the opportunity to show the foreign readers a little bit of life in America, a life that I treasure.

In many ways, how we view cicadas is quite similar to how we treat people we do not understand. When we are not familiar with someone or something, we often view them with suspicion, misgiving, misunderstanding, or even discrimination. But in reality, most people are just like us -- innocent, warm-hearted, peaceful, and fun-loving. If we can learn to give everyone the benefit of the doubt, then our families, society, and the whole world may be a lot happier and more peaceful.

Finally, I would like to express my deepest gratitude to everyone involved in the creation of this book. I feel that this is not just an accomplishment for the artist and me, but also many other people who are passionate about cicadas who we have never even met. These friends are American, Chinese, Japanese, and many other nationalities, and they selflessly and very willingly provided valuable pictures and material that really touched me. I would like to let the readers know that this generosity and enthusiastic spirit can be seen everywhere (and not just in looking at cicadas).

Forward

I guess this is somewhat my fault. During a family dinner several years ago, I was briefly explaining what I had been doing with my spare time and I took that as an opportunity to explain what a webcomic is. It is essentially a comic, similar to the ones you find in the Sunday newspaper only in a digital format. Mine only had an inkling of success which was apparently enough for my father to want to make something of his own.

For my father this story probably begins during his childhood years. He had humble beginnings and did not have much to play with that was not found, nor made. To him, cicadas were free, loud, and could be caught and played with. One might be able to compare them to a popular doll that laughs when you tickle it. Compared to a doll though, cicadas were far more plentiful, very much free, and far more appealing to my father.

And so some number of years later my father decided he wanted to make a comic book about cicadas. It should be noted that he has little knowledge of comics outside of the "Sunday Funnies," and has read less than a handful of American novels. My father does not draw, and only speaks English with moderate sufficiency. That said, I admire my father very much. He has lived the American dream with far less to start with. He has pulled himself up from his own bootstraps and has had successes that I can only hope to duplicate.

This book, as it stands, is a testament to what you can accomplish regardless of who criticizes you and by how much. If nothing else, this book shows that with enough passion, drive, and determination you can make nearly anything a reality.

Franklin Shian
Designer
Son

In the Eastern United States, there is a special type of cicada that emerges every 17 years. They are called "periodical cicadas," and they belong to the genus Magicicada.

▲ ▼ Photos Courtesy of Edward Delaplaine

Those cicadas appeared in 2004, 1987, 1970, etc. and are expected to appear in 2021 and 2038 are called Brood X. Brood X is the largest of the 17-year broods, and they are expected to emerge in the following states: DC, DE, GA, IL, IN, KY, MA, MD, MI, NC, NJ, NY, OH, PA, TN, VA, and WV.

◄ Photos Courtesy of Davy Shian

These red-eye cicadas were impressive as they emerged in billions.

► ▲ Photos Courtesy of Craig Froehle

Photos Courtesy of Tammy Bianchi ▼ ▶

One cicada is noisy already; imagine when there are billions of them singing at the same time.

Periodical Cicadas

▼ **Photo Courtesy of Lester Daniels**

Those cicadas that appeared in 1974, 1991, etc. and expected to appear in 2008, 2025, and 2042 are called Brood XIV. Affected states are KY, GA, IN, MA, MD, NC, NJ, NY, OH, PA,TN,VA, WVA.

The periodical cicadas consist of broods of 13-year and 17-year.

13-year Broods

Brood	Year				General region
XIX	1972	1985	1998	2011	AL, AR, GA, IN, IL, KY, LA, MD, MO, MS, NC, OK, SC, TN, TX, VA
XXII	1975	1988	2001	2014	LA, MS
XXIII	1976	1989	2002	2015	AR, IL, IN, KY, LA, MO, MS, TN

17-year Broods

Brood	Year				General region
I	1961	1978	1995	2012	VA, WV
II	1962	1979	1996	2013	CT, MD, NC, NJ, NY, PA, VA
III	1963	1980	1997	2014	IA, IL, MO
IV	1964	1981	1998	2015	IA, KS, MO, NE, OK, TX
V	1965	1982	1999	2016	MD, OH, PA, VA, WV
VI	1966	1983	2000	2017	GA, NC, SC
VII	1967	1984	2001	2018	NY
VIII	1968	1985	2002	2019	OH, PA, WV
IX	1969	1986	2003	2020	NC, VA, WV
X	1970	1987	2004	2021	DE, GA, IL, IN, KY, MD, MI, NC, NJ, NY, OH, PA, TN, VA, WV
XIII	1973	1990	2007	2024	IA, IL, IN, MI, WI
XIV	1974	1991	2008	2025	KY, GA, IN, MA, MD, NC, NJ, NY, OH, PA, TN, VA, WV

Table of Contents

Main Characters

Dave is a Chinese American who has loved cicadas since childhood. He acts as a messenger providing interesting cicada information.

Bill represents those who hate cicadas because his home was infested with cicadas.

Paula represents those single ladies who dislike bugs.

John represents those who are curious about cicadas.

Mary represents children who are just getting to know about cicadas.

Cicadas are the main character that needs to be understood.

1. HOW DO YOU FEEL ABOUT CICADAS?

The year 1987, 2004, 2021 on the US, East Coast...

In other news, the 17 year cicada is scheduled to arrive very shortly...

Our listeners please take note; the red-eye cicada is coming.
Dave, the 17-year cicadas will be emerging soon; many people are worried about it. Do you like cicadas?
I love cicadas. They remind me of my childhood in Taiwan. There's nothing to worry about.

I remember...
back in the old days, we didn't have fancy toys so we played with those noisy cicadas.
Hey look what I just got!
Yahhh! Get it away from me!
Oh, you were mean.
Paula, I was only trying to share my toys.

2. HOW DO YOU CATCH CICADAS?

It's not easy to catch a cicada.

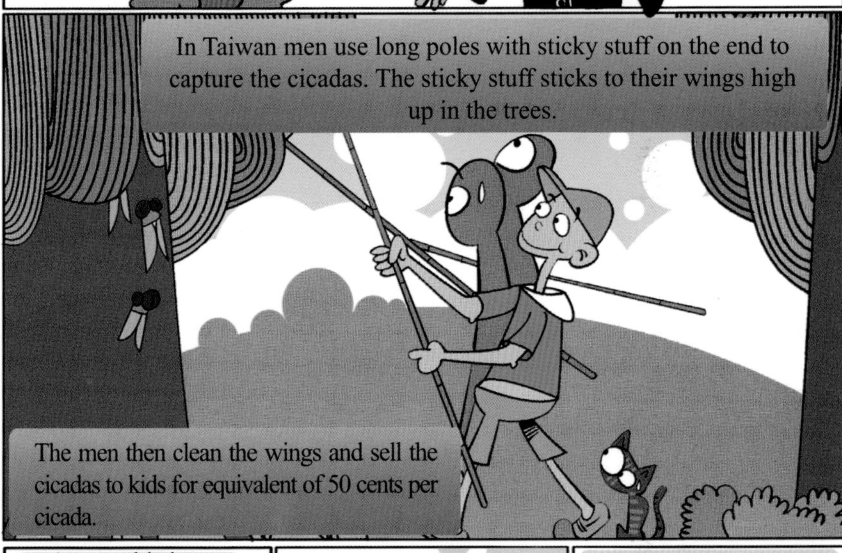

In Taiwan men use long poles with sticky stuff on the end to capture the cicadas. The sticky stuff sticks to their wings high up in the trees.
The men then clean the wings and sell the cicadas to kids for equivalent of 50 cents per cicada.

Awww this is a female. I don't want it. It doesn't make any noise.

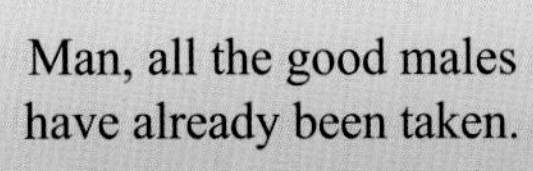

Man, all the good males have already been taken.

It seems that good men are hard to find even in the insect kingdom.

3. THE UNIQUENESS OF THE 17-YEAR CICADAS

Hey, Bill, do you know where I can get a camouflage outfit and a long bamboo stick?
Why?
I heard that the cicadas are out, and I want to catch some for my kid to play with.
Are you kidding?! You don't need all that! Come to my house after work.
Later at Bill's...
Help yourself.
I guess America really DOES have more of everything!
Htzzzssssssssssssssssssssss Htzzzsssssssssssssssss Htzzs

4. THE FRENCH VIEW OF CICADAS

Argh! These cicadas are everywhere!
Bill, why do you detest cicadas so much?

Do you know that people in Provence, France think cicadas are a good luck charm -- so much so that they made the cicadas the symbol of Provence? They have cicada post cards, cicada fabrics, cicada candles, cicada soaps, cicada jewelry; and many homes have a ceramic cicada near the entrance door or inside the home for good luck.

Since you have so many cicadas at your home, you should consider it as having lots of good luck.

Yeah right, I'm just really, really lucky... With this kind of luck I should play the lottery more often.

5. SOME PEOPLE JUST DON'T LIKE CICADAS

So Bill, why so much disdain for cicadas?
I'll show you.
So what do you think?
Help me!
AHHH!
Man, she can really fly. She should be a track star.

6. WHY CHINESE LIKE CICADAS

Why do the Chinese like cicadas so much?
Can I join you guys?
Hi John, we are talking about cicadas.
See, I think it's all very poetic. Chinese poets love to visit the mountains for tranquility; the singing of cicadas bring out the quietness of the mountain. Some poets loved to include cicadas in their poems, so, when other people read the poems, they got a good impression of the cicadas.
HttzzsssssssHtzsssssssss
HttzzsssssssHtzzzssss
HtssssssHtzzzsssssssss
Tranquility, huh? Were they listening to the same cicadas as I am?

7. WHY CICADAS MUST BE HUMBLE

Tell me how the poets described the cicadas.
One of the poems says that the cicada antennas look like a Chinese scholar's hat, so it symbolizes intellect. It breathes fresh air and drinks only dew so it is pure.
It does not covet wheat and rice so it is honest. It lives without housing so it is frugal. It has a sense of timing and therefore is dependable.
It is an insect with the most virtue.
Are you really that good?
I would have said yes, but humbleness is also a virtue.

8. THE BRITISH VIEW OF CICADAS

Do you know the British also think cicadas are examples of moral goodness?
In the 16th century, British entomologist Thomas Moufet wrote, "It eats nothing belonging to the earth and drinks only dew, proving cleanliness, purity and propriety; it will not accept wheat or rice, thus indicating its probity and honesty! It appears always at a fixed time, showing it is endowed with fidelity, sincerity and truthfulness."
Where did you get that?
The Internet.
I think either this was made up, or Moufet was a relative of your Chinese poet.
Why do you say that?
First of all, the two said almost the same thing, and second, why would the British emphasize rice?
How could anyone make this up?
Shouldn't we have more virtue than the cicadas...?

9. SOME HOMES DON'T HAVE CICADAS

Cicadas are disgusting. They are all over my house, the backyard, the driveway, even on my car tires. When I drive I crush them and make a mess. I spent so much time cleaning them and the very next day, they're back.
But there are so many amazing things about cicadas.
Boy, are they noisy. I'm glad they are quiet at night.
It's fun watching the nymphs emerge and molt.
No fair! I haven't seen any cicada at my new house. I want my share of cicadas.

You live in a new development. When the builders disturbed the ground, they killed the larvae.
I have an idea. Why don't we swap homes for two months?
Alright! Agreed.

10. HOW CICADAS HELP A LITTLE GIRL SLEEP

Daddy, Daddy, I can’t sleep. I’m afraid of the cicadas.
Don't worry dear. The cicadas are so pretty; they have big red eyes, a shiny body, and pretty wings. They don't attack people and they don't bite.
They emerge from their ugly shells and become so beautiful, just like how Cinderella turned into a princess.
If you still can't sleep try counting cicadas...
One thousand, Two Thousand, Three Thousand…

11. A SAMPLE OF THE 17-YEAR CICADAS

Hi boss, so being from the U.K. you've not seen the 17-year cicadas, have you?
No, but maybe you can grab me a sample tomorrow.
Morning, boss.
Good morning.

YOWZA!

I asked for a sample, not a whole trash can!!!
Well, a sample from a billion is a trash can full.
It wasn't even hard to get.

12. CICADA TRICKS FOR ATTRACTING MATES

Did you know that the male cicada sings to attract a female?
Haven't heard that one before.

Want to study together?

How come John is obsessed in showing his lady friends cicadas?

Well, John has been lonely, and he thought he could use the cicada's song to charm the ladies.

No date again?
No.

We love you!
Go away!

13. CICADA, YOU ARE NOT HELPING

It's so hot, let's have a drink.
Httzsssss

Cicada! Ahhh!

You did that on purpose. You jerk.

There goes my chance for a date tonight.

You're no help at all.
Hey I'm not a great flier yet. At least I didn't fall in her cup.

14. CICADA SHELLS ARE USED IN MEDICINE

Did you know that the Chinese use cicada shells for medicine?
Really?
Hmmm...
Hi Paula, do you notice anything different about me?
Well, your eyes seem a bit bulgy and red. Have you been drinking all night?

15. THE LEAVES ARE FALLING EARLY THIS YEAR

Have you noticed? For some reason, the leaves are falling very early this year.
Crunch
Crunch
Oh, those aren't leaves. They're the cicada shells.

Carry me! Carry me! Carry me!

Sh-sure thing, Paula.

16. SUMMER SOUND

Ring
Ring
Ring

Hey Dave, What are you up to?
Watching a Japanese soap opera with my wife.
Many times they use cicada sounds to indicate that it's summer time.

Listen...

Summerrr Tiiimmmmme
And the wind is breezy...

And I thought it was a bad sound effect.

17. SO WHAT'S DIFFERENT ABOUT A DISH OF CICADAS?

So many choices, I don't know what to pick.
I love shrimp, adore crab, raw oysters are outstanding and snails are exquisite.
There is a new dish called cicada with blue crab sauce. Want to try it?
Cicada? No way! Just the thought makes me want to puke.
I am not encouraging you to eat cicadas, but I don't understand your reaction.
Crabs and lobsters are scavengers that eat stuff I wouldn't.
Out of sight, out of mind.
They also have higher cholesterol than cicadas.

18. WHAT DO CICADAS REALLY TASTE LIKE?

Cicadas were eaten in Ancient Greece, China, Burma, Australia, North and South America, and the Congo. Many say cicadas are delicious and taste like nuts. Want to give it a try?
No way, but let's find a college student to try it on. They're curious and will eat anything.

Hey, do you want to try something cool?
Alright.
Well, how's the taste?
Tastes like dirt.

Really?

What do you expect? I'd taste like dirt too after living in the ground for 17 years!

19. HOW IT PAYS TO DO A GOOD DEED

Hey there. Why are you collecting cicada shells?

I'm doing it for community service. I want to keep the environment clean.

Night market in Asia.

Special sale! A pill that has the ingredient of the American 17-year cicada shells that will make you live 10 years longer!

I want one.

Give me a bag.

Give me one too.

It pays to do a good deed.
Ha!

20. WHAT EATS CICADAS?

Htzzssssss

Htssss

It's a good thing there are billions of cicadas.

I hope many will survive.

21. WHAT IS A CICADA KILLER WASP?

Why so down?
Do you know that cicadas get eaten by almost every animal?
It's not fair.
Did you know that there is another bug that is feasting on cicadas?
The Cicada Killer Wasp.
That's me.
The female stings and paralyzes a cicada. Then it lays an egg on the cicada...
... and has her baby larva feed on it.
How sad! Good guys are always the first to go.
Worse yet...
…the cicada-killer is considered a beneficial insect because it keeps populations down.
Bad bug
Bad bug
Bad bug
Bad bug
Beneficial insect because it kills defenseless cicadas? We need a revote!!!

22. HEARD OF CICADA BIRDS?

Mmm I love to eat cicadas.
It's like an all you can eat buffet.
Whoo! I'm so full I can hardly fly.
I love to eat birds.
Have you caught any "Cicada Birds?" They are fat and juicy and very tasty.
Too bad that this breed only shows up once every 17 years!

23. BIRD EVASION

One way to avoid being caught by a bird during flying is to fly in circles. That makes it difficult for the bird to catch us.

A bird is coming!
I know how to get away now.

!
!!!

Listen, he did well except for not hearing the vital statement before rushing out -- we also need to pay attention to where the bird is.

24. DO YOU WATCH YOUR BACK?

There is a Chinese story of a mantis that was hunting a cicada. At the same time, a bird was hunting the mantis, but the mantis was too focused on the cicada to notice and was eaten. The lesson of the story is "watch your back."
OK, I got it...
WHOA!
Hot chicks! Let's follow them.
You should slow down... there's a cop behind us.
The best way to learn is to experience it. I guess...

25. DISAPPEARING ACT

Look, a big meal. Let's surround it and attack it during day light.
It has stopped to rest. This should be a piece of cake.
Here I come.
Strange, there's no meat!
How do you like my disappearing act?

26. WHAT'S A CAT'S FAVORITE FOOD?

VETERINARY SERVICES

Doctor, I think my baby kitty is sick. She hasn't eaten her favorite food of milk and fish for almost a week.

She looks healthy...
Let me take a look.

She's alright, except that her favorite food is really cicada, and her stomach is full of them.

Cicada, *prrrrr...*

27. A CICADA LAWYER?

Htssss
Yah!
Crunch
Lady, you hit a fire hydrant. I'm going to write you a ticket.
It's the cicada's fault, you should give it the ticket.
I am innocent! I need a lawyer.
Me!
No win, no charge.

28. ARE CICADAS DANGEROUS?

Cicadas are dangerous.
Why is that?

Paula got a cicada in her hair while driving, and it caused her to hit a fire hydrant.

I heard a kid fell off his bike trying to avoid a cicada.

Worst of all, my dog is constipated because he ate so many cicada shells.

If you fed your dog better, it wouldn't have to eat cicada shells.

I agree 100% with John.

29. WHAT IS CICADA PHOBIA?

Having a party?
No, I am rescuing my aunt from hunger.
She's very afraid of bugs, and with the emergence of the 17 year cicadas, she has been held captive in her own home.
knock knock
Who's there?
It's John with your food.
Are they still out there?
Yup, they will be for a few more weeks.
Oh, my God!
This is getting ridiculous. Am I going to have to do this every day until the cicadas are gone?

30. CICADA NICKNAMES

DEAD WRONG!
LOCUST

WE DON'T SUCK BLOOD!
VAMPI
BUG

FEROCIOUS BUG
NOT EVEN CLOSE.

UGLY BUG
MAN, GIVE US A BREAK.

Bird of Rehua. Rehua is lord of kindness and plenty.

PRETTY GOOD, BUT ONLY NEW ZEALANDERS WOULD GET IT.

How about we call you Love Bug?

WE CAN LIVE WITH THAT!

31. ARE CICADAS CLUMSY?

Htssss
Htssss
You know cicadas are really stupid and clumsy fliers. They easily fall from the sky or they fly into things.
Really? How long did it take for you to learn to walk? Or ride a bicycle? Don't tell me you never fell down.
Cicadas have to fly with no practice, so don't call MY cicadas stupid and clumsy!!
He reacted like I was talking about his son.

32. WOULD YOU BET ON A CICADA?

Look, a cicada is hanging on the antenna.
I bet it can't hold on for long.

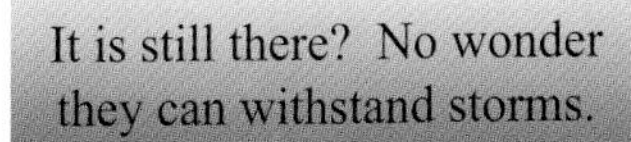
It is still there? No wonder they can withstand storms.

Hey you're speeding! And there's a cop on our back.

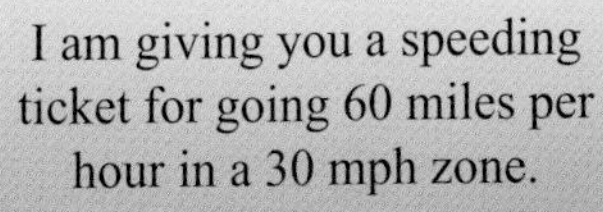
The car is going 65 mile/hr, he drives fast!

I am giving you a speeding ticket for going 60 miles per hour in a 30 mph zone.

You have to pay up when you lose a bet.

33. ANY PITY FOR CICADAS?

Htssss
Httzsssss
I'm happy to see you have changed your opinion of cicadas. I know you felt bad for the cicadas when you hit them.
I was worrying about my car.

In late May when the ground temperature is 64° F, the cicadas climb up and molt. The false eye spots are designed to deter predators.

*Photos Courtesy of Edward Delaplaine

Initially their body is pale-white. After a couple of hours, the cicada's body will begin to darken and its wings will harden and fold over its back.

***Photos Courtesy of Edward Delaplaine**

The adult cicada grows up to three inches long.

***Photos Courtesy of Edward Delaplaine**

34. NYMPH INTO AN ADULT

I really want to see the nymph change into a mature cicada.
Do you mind? Some privacy please? I can't shed when I'm being watched.
I'll dim the lights and pretend to be a tree.

35. HAVE PATIENCE?

Want to see the pictures I took?

What are they?
It took me hours just to get 6 pictures.
They're pictures of a cicada emerging from its shell and becoming an adult!

Wow John, are you as patient when waiting for a woman to get ready?
Sure, as long as his woman is as good looking as a cicada.

36. ARE YOU A GOOD PERSON?

Why did so many of my cicadas fail to molt, or had misshapen wings, or got stuck in their shell?
It's probably because you liked to play with them. It took a lot of energy for the cicadas to emerge, and your playing with them tired them out.
I'm a cicada baby killer. I must redeem myself.
RIP
RIP
RIP
RIP
RIP

I can tell that John is a good guy because he cares so much.

37. A GREAT BABY PICTURE

Baby pictures are great. Kids just grow up so fast.
I just wish we had some way to record the year.
What about taking pictures with the cicadas? Everyone will easily identify the year.
I have an idea.
Look at this. Great picture!!

38. WHAT'S YOUR FOCUS?

I am taking some nature pictures, would you like to help?
Sure.
click
click
click
click
click
I don't see myself.
Sorry the main focus was the cicada.
Don't you ever talk to me again!

39. THE INSECT COMPETITION

The MOST Resourceful Insect Competition
I have a compound eye, and I can easily spot any movement. I am a strong flyer, and I can capture my prey in a second.

We have strong jaws, and although we are small, an army of us can eat up anything in our way.

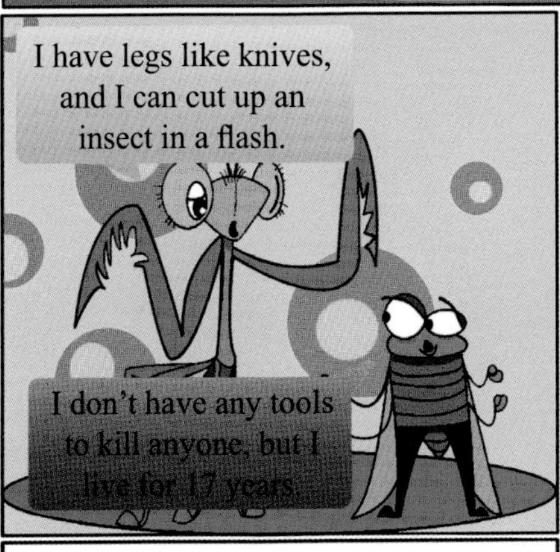
I have legs like knives, and I can cut up an insect in a flash.
I don't have any tools to kill anyone, but I live for 17 years.

1
The winner!

Unfair!
BOOO!
Hiss!
Bias!

Well with all your weapons, why couldn't you live for 17 years...

40. NEED ENVIRONMENTALISTS

The 17-year cicada species is known as Brood X. It evolved from the 13-year cicada brood.
Do you know the reason why they developed an extra four-year dormancy period?
No, but I can imagine a reason.
I see where the new houses and roads will be built. We will need to add 4 more years to our project plan for emerging.

41. CICADAS CAN SEE WELL

I wonder if a cicada can see, or if those big red eyes are just fakes to scare away the predators.
Please move your hand! I can prove that I see very well.

It is none of your business!
Go concentrate on something else.
I can tell that she is wearing a thong... What's the purpose of wearing a thong?

About your makeup...

You nasty little bug, get out of here before I squash you and your big red eyes.

42. A TEENAGER'S DILEMMA

It's climbing up!
Yes, it is shedding.
It's flying away...

It has been 17 years. Finally. I want to sing for life!

I saw him first, he's mine.
Don't touch him, he's mine.
No you don't, he is mine.

So this is what I have been waiting for!

43. AN IDOL CONTEST

LOVE SONG CONTEST
Well, you have high pitch, and your love song might be lovely. But in order to be a star, your look just won't do it.
What do you think about the judge's harsh comment?
Too bad my cicada friends are more into mating than voting; otherwise I would have surely won.

 44. WHAT IS CICADA RAIN?

Rare Blue-Eyed Cicada and Silver-Eyed Cicada (The unique eye colors were caused by a genetic variation.)

Photos Courtesy of Gaye Williams ▲ ▶

Did you notice that the cicada shells all face inward?

***Photo Courtesy of Davy Shian**

45. ANOTHER CICADA MYSTERY

Everyone! While going out, please climb as high as you can to make room for others. There are billions of us, and we need plenty of room to molt.
When you have gone as far as you can such as to an edge of a leaf, turn around and molt there. Never go back because it would cause confusion and a big traffic jam.
Do you notice that the cicada shells are all facing inward? Ever wonder why?
Yeah, only problem is nobody knows.

46. LIKE NATURAL CONFETTI?

Htssss
Htssss
Httzsssss
Httzsssss
Htzzssssss
Htzzssssss
Httzsssss
Htssss
Htzzssssss

Hey cousin, today is your big day. Why do you look so upset?
Look at these cicadas. They're going to ruin my wedding.
They're flying and singing because they're looking for love, it's actually quite fitting.

Just think of them as natural confetti.

47. IF ONLY WE HAD WINGS

Today's homework is to create something imaginary. Use any safe material you can find in your home.
Mary, this is a great work. I especially like those lovely wings. Where did you get so many pretty wings?
Oh, those were from dead cicadas.
Ewww! Cicadas!!!

48. UMBRELLA ON A SUNNY DAY?

Why the umbrella? I thought you loved sun tans.
The umbrella is for the cicadas. I don't want them on me, dead or alive.
It's really not that horrible.
What the…?
OH NO!
Can I share this umbrella with you? Bird droppings are worse.

49. WHAT DID KUNG FU MASTER LEARN?

Some kung fu methods were derived from animals such as the “Tiger Claws,” the “Snake Fists,” the “Crane Boxing,” and the “Praying Mantis Chop.”
I also got one concept from cicadas that you must learn. The calm cicada lives for 17 years but the cicada that has sex only lives for a few weeks...

We need kung fu masters! My movie needs special fighting skills and the story also requires passionate kissing with our female star.
Bruce
No way, I can’t do that.

Well, I don’t know how.
Jet

Jackie
No problem. We can always get a stunt man for the love scene.

50. THE UP OR DOWN QUESTION

Your drawing is wrong. Cicadas always face up, not down.
No, you're wrong; they sometimes face down.

No need to argue; let me show you.

The answer is quite obvious. To be a successful artist, you must be observant.

Cicadas sing to attract a mate. These cicadas mate after singing.

***Photo Courtesy of Davy Shian**

Then she lays eggs. You can see the "ovipositor" jammed into the tree branch. This is the dark 1cm length tube coming out of her abdomen, behind the 4 back legs.

▲ Photo Courtesy of Edward Delaphaine

The oviposited branches become weak and break off easily by wind currents. The leaves of these damaged branches also turn brown which creates what is commonly referred to as "Flagging."

▲ Photo Courtesy of Tammy Bianchi

It takes about 6 to 8 weeks for the eggs to hatch, and the nymphs will move underground where they live for 17 years.

***Photos Courtesy of Gaye Williams**

17 years later, they come out of the soil and become adults.

Photo Courtesy of Dan Henderson ▶

◀ Photo Courtesy of Edward Delaphaine

51. DO YOU TRIM YOUR HAIR?

I noticed that many of my trees' leaves are turning brown and breaking.
That's probably caused by female cicadas.

When the female lays her eggs on a branch, the leaves will turn brown and the branch will snap in strong winds.

Ha! This should qualify the cicada as a pest.
pest

Let's not jump to that conclusion so quickly. We don't mind having a trim once in a while. Cicadas provide a service for us.

I love my new look. Do you call hair stylists pests?

No, we pay them big bucks.

52. WHAT ARE CICADAS GOOD FOR?

Daddy, what are cicadas good for?
Well, they dig holes, which is good for the soil. When they die, they also provide nutrition for the soil. They provide food for animals, even people.
And most important of all, they provide entertainment for all.

Love is such a splendid thing.

53. LOVE CAN BE SO DIFFERENT

Splash

Take my advice, use cicadas as bait. They are very effective.

Never! I love cicadas.

Another one. This is great! I LOVE cicadas.
Love? This is not the way to show love.

Ladies, be careful when Bill says he loves you.

54. TREASURE YOUR CICADA BELT

fooosh

I hope you like this special present.

Oh, it's a belt with a big cicada buckle. Thanks, I like it.

...but I will never wear it.

You know that cicada belt is very special and rare. Chinese feel wearing a belt with a cicada on it will bring wealth, and every Chinese would love to have one.

Really? In that case I will wear it every day.

55. CICADAS AND THE ECONOMY?

This article says that souvenir vendors are selling cicada T-shirts and jewelry stores are selling cicada pins and earrings.
... The hardware store can't keep up with the demand for cicada nets, and the car washes are packed.
People all over are coming to watch the cicadas. The economy is doing great!
Let me check the stock prices.
For the sake of my rising stock portfolio, I should start liking cicadas.

56. MISSION IMPOSSIBLE

Mr. President, our opponent is making significant gains because of the issues on war, education, and the environment. But it looks like cicadas are turning around the economy, and this gives us an excellent chance for re-election.
This is great news! Do you have a plan?
Yes sir.
Let's get started then.
Your mission is to find a way to make cicadas live past the election. This tape will self-destruct in 5 seconds.
beep
beep

57. THE ISSUE OF DISCRIMINATION

You know, although Americans say we are still having discrimination problems, I feel things are getting better, and it's certainly better than a lot of other countries.
We should be. We have laws that prohibit discrimination. And our kids are being taught to be more aware of it.
Look, a cicada is listening to us talking.
Yak! I hate bugs. Get rid of it! Kill it!
What happened to no discrimination?
America should have a law prohibiting discrimination against bugs.

58. MEMBERS OF THE CICADA CLUB

Dave, I found an online cicada club and joined it.

How was it?

I discovered that there were lots of people who loved to talk about cicadas. I've been getting over 100 emails a day. My mailbox is almost full.

So are you going to quit?

No way, I love it! Nobody ever emails me.
You should join this cicada club. Members love to hear our stories. I've sent hundreds of emails already.

59. THE ANNUAL CICADAS

Daddy, it's so quiet. There are no cicadas singing any more. Are the cicadas really gone?
I'm afraid so. But they'll come back in 17 years.
17 years is so long.
A few weeks later...
Daddy, daddy, I heard a cicada singing. Are they back?
No dear, these are different cicadas. But since you like cicadas so much they'll come visit you every summer.
Yay!!

60. ITALIAN GOD CREATED CICADA

There is an ancient Italian myth about cicadas...
There was a beautiful, good, and very talented woman whose singing was so wonderful that it even enchanted the gods.

So when she died, the world was so forlorn that the gods recreated her as a cicada so that her singing could once again lift the hearts of everyone.

That is such a pretty story.

That Italian God made a big mistake. Only the male cicadas sing.

61. DIFFERENT CICADA SOUNDS?

Can you distinguish different cicada sounds?

I heard one in my yard that sounded like "rrrrrRRRRR-atatat TAT TAT TAT TAT TAT."
I heard one going "Wheeeeee-Oooooooh."
I heard "rat tat tat tat buzz and tss tss tss tss tss tss tss."
I heard one that went "eeeeeeee-Eeer-EeerEeeer-EEEERееееееeeee."
I love Wheeeeee-Ooooooh. It drives me crazy.

62. HAVE YOU SEEN A GHOST?

Someone saw a ghost early this morning. I'm going to investigate tomorrow. Want to join me?
Sure; sounds interesting.

I see a shadow. Is it the ghost?
It sure is moving fast, and it's coming right at us.

RUN!

It's John! What are you doing here?
I was told I could find annual cicada nymphs around the cemetery's ash trees. Instead, I encountered a skunk. Man, it scared me.
Not sure who's scaring who. Everyone thought you're a ghost.

63. WHY IT IS OK TO BE SILLY

WHEEEEEoooooooo... WHHEEEEEoooooo...
What does that mean?
The cicada club members send it in e-mails to say good morning.
You guys are crazy.

Well, I guess I'd rather be warm-and-silly than cold-and-indifferent.
Funny, I thought I heard my Romeo. Where is he?

64. WHAT WOMEN WANT

I don't know what attracts women today. The looks? The money? The body? The brain? The heart? Time?
I also heard that women want a little bad boy too. It's so confusing.
You should learn from our success, just sing and it brings on the ladies.
OK, I'll try.
What is that terrible noise? I can't stand it. Let's get out of here.

65. AREN'T BABIES ADORABLE?

Do you love babies?
Sure. Babies are so cute, so innocent, and so helpless.

You know those are the same reasons that I love cicadas. Cicadas are probably cleaner than babies, and I don't have to worry about feeding them.
Well Cicadas sing, mate and then die. Babies grow up to be people. I'll stick to loving babies.

But when babies grow up, they'll also fly away.

66. WOMEN LOVE CICADAS

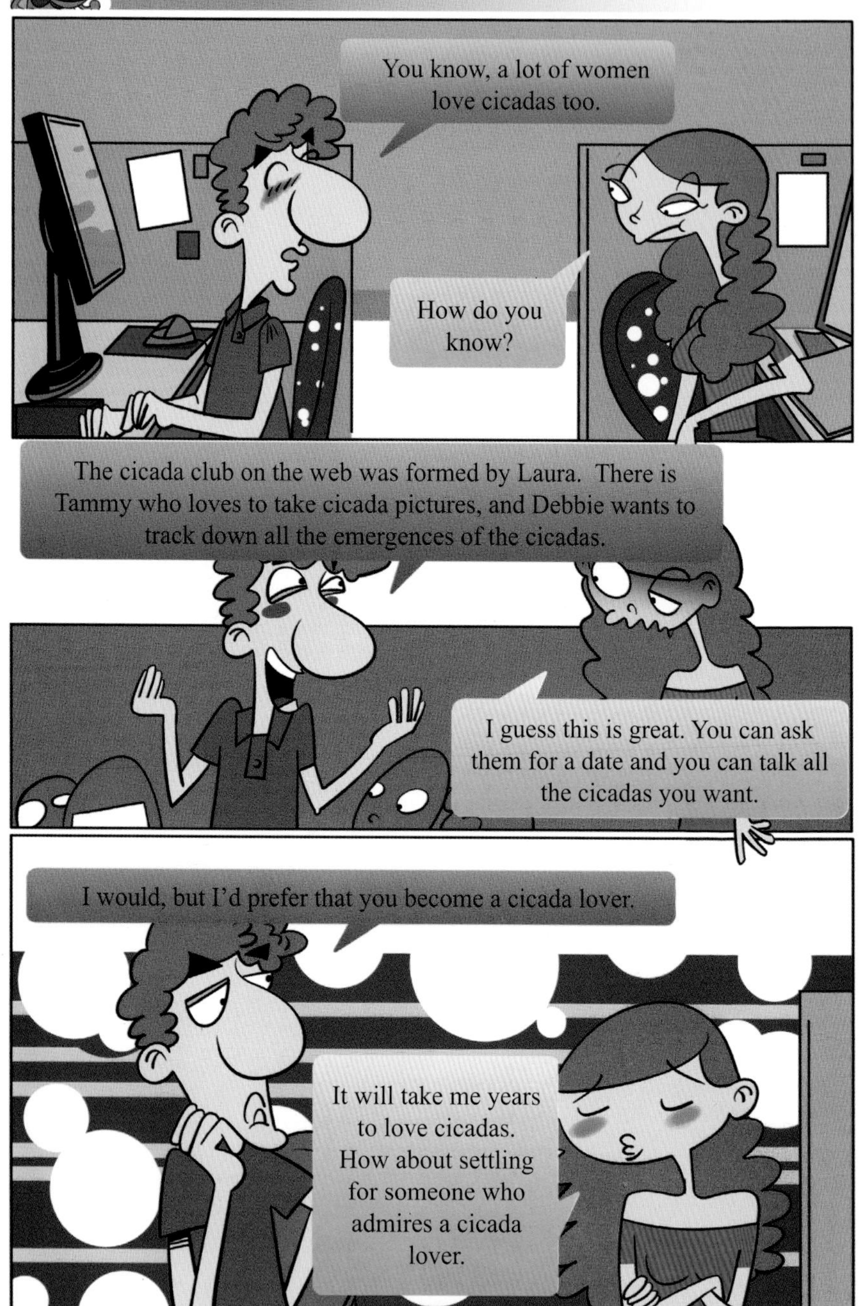

You know, a lot of women love cicadas too.
How do you know?
The cicada club on the web was formed by Laura. There is Tammy who loves to take cicada pictures, and Debbie wants to track down all the emergences of the cicadas.
I guess this is great. You can ask them for a date and you can talk all the cicadas you want.
I would, but I'd prefer that you become a cicada lover.
It will take me years to love cicadas. How about settling for someone who admires a cicada lover.

67. THE RIGHT HOLE

The annual cicadas are hard to find. To find the nymphs, look at the base of old trees, and search for dime-size holes.
This hole is a little bigger. Perhaps more nymphs were in there. I'll pay extra attention to this one.
I'm hungry; let's go out to get some food.
Hold on. There's a human outside peeking at us. Let's wait until he gets distracted by something else.
See? That didn't take long.

68. THE CICADA POLL RESULTS

My cicada opinion polls are in: 10% of people love cicadas 30% dislike them and 60% don't care.
60%
30%
10%
I think we need to do some campaign work. We need to emphasize that cicadas are full of love. We value peace, and cicadas are peaceful insects. The 17-year cicada is OUR insect because only we have it and we should love and support our symbol.
Our campaign worked! A new cicada poll result is out: 70% love cicadas 20% dislike them 10 % still have no opinion
You know, we really should campaign for Bug of the World.

69. LONG LIVE THE CICADAS

I am a cicada geek. I would drive 1000 miles just to see cicadas.
I am a cicada geek. I collect everything about cicadas.
I am a cicada geek. I can tell different species just by their sound.
I am a cicada geek. I learn and do what I can to protect cicadas.

LONG LIVE THE CICADAS!
I think the fact we are talking about it means we all qualify as cicada geeks. Hail to the cicadas.

American Annual Cicadas (Annual cicadas also spend several years underground before emerging but some emerge every year, not just every 17 years.)

◀ ▼ Photos Courtesy of Gerry Bunker

▲ Photos Courtesy of Virginia Senechal

▲ Photos Courtesy of Davy Shian

Photos Courtesy of...

▲ 陈帆(Xdai)

▲ 吴銘進

▲ John Moore

▲ 郑北巽

▲ Davy Shian

▼ Susumu Kaino

Asian cicadas

▼ 陳佳欣

Below is Chinese character for cicada (pronounced as "tzan?"), and it has 14 strokes.

When you see cicadas, do you look at their ugly side...

***Photos Courtesy of Davy Shian**

Or do you look at their beautiful side?

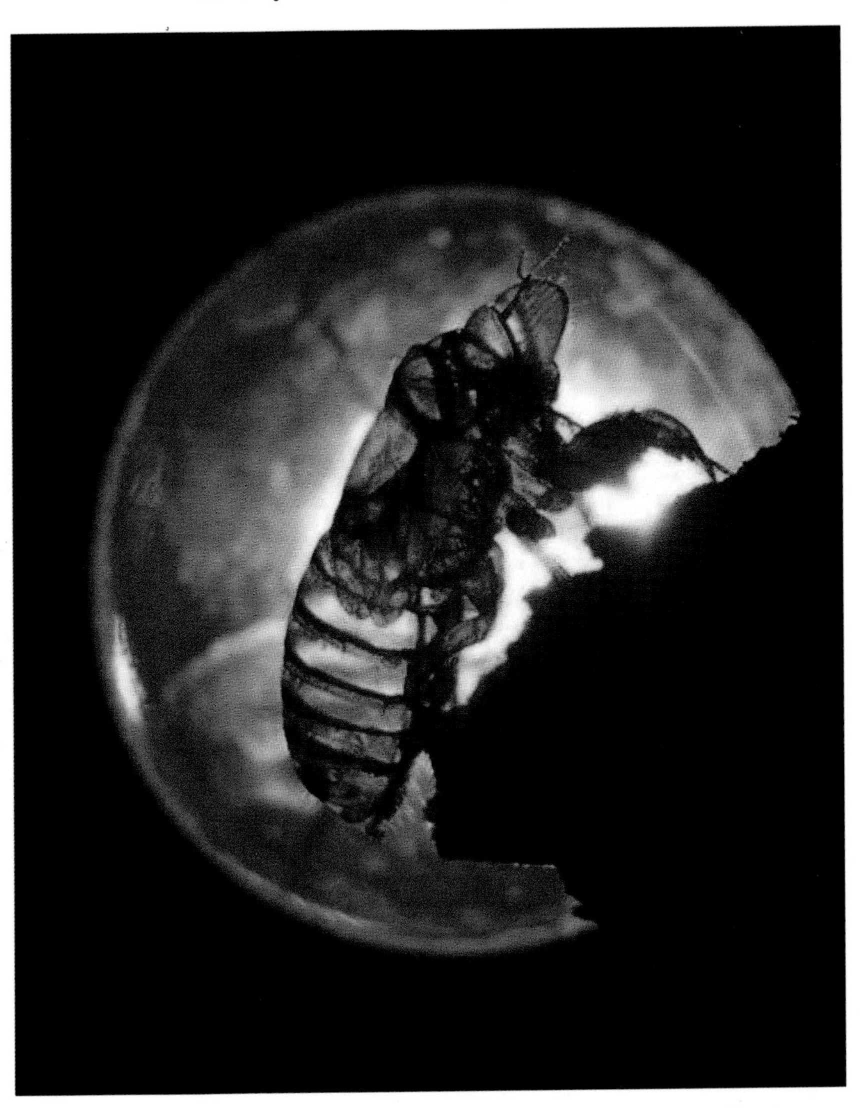

***Photos Courtesy of Dan Henderson**

Special Thanks to those provided us with unselfish and enthusiastic support

Alex Anderson
Tammy Bianchi
Gerry Bunker
Lester Daniels
Edward Delaplaine
Craig Froehle
Dan Henderson
Susumu Kaino
John Moore
Virginia Senechal
Rob Stotz
Jamie Tang
Gaye Williams, Maryland Department of Agriculture
Laura Woodswalker
Xtin Xtin

陈磊
陈帆
陳佳欣
張彦哲
張思敬
吳銘進
郑北異
郭玉京
任彦娜
王凤岭
郭小胜

The following websites have abundant information on cicadas:

http://www.cicadamania.com

http://members.fortunecity.com/cicadaman1999/id27.htm

http://en.wikipedia.org/wiki/Magicicada

http://homepage.mac.com/akbar/magicicada2004/index.html

http://abbot.si.edu/highlight/cicadas/faq.htm

http://www.indiana.edu/~preserve/research/CicadasPres/slide14.html#

http://www.inhs.uiuc.edu/highlights/periodicalCicada.html

http://insects.ummz.lsa.umich.edu/fauna/michigan_cicadas/Periodical/

THE END

To contact us about this book:

cicadabook@gmail.com

图书在版编目（CIP）数据

蝉的面面观：英文／大卫·项著；王星绘.—石家庄：河北美术出版社，2008.5
ISBN 978-7-5310-3093-5

Ⅰ. 蝉… Ⅱ.①项…②王… Ⅲ.蝉科-普及读物-英文
Ⅳ.Q969.36-49

中国版本图书馆CIP数据核字（2008）第049178号

蝉的面面观

出版发行	河北美术出版社
地　　址	石家庄市和平西路新文里8号
邮政编码	050071
印　　刷	保定市彩虹艺雅印刷有限公司
开　　本	889×1194毫米 1/32
印　　张	3.25
印　　数	1-1200
书　　号	ISBN 978-7-5310-3093-5
版　　次	2008年5月第1版
印　　次	2008年5月第1次印刷
定　　价	USA $14.99